The Greenwich Roll of Honour
1914-1918

Published 100 years after the end of the First World War

Edited by Rob Powell

Foreword by the Revd Canon Chris Moody

In St Alfege Church we have 167 names, including two families, the Sewells and the Baulsons who lost four members each. Herbert, Harry, Henry and Cecil (who was awarded a posthumous VC) in the case of the Sewells, and John, Henry, Richard and George in the case of the Baulsons.

It is important to give these people back their individual names as a reminder that war is not just a general tragedy, or a big event in the history books, but made up of trauma, interruption and disclocation in the lives of individual families of ordinary people. What must it have been like for the Sewells and Baulsons to sustain such loss? I had an uncle I never knew killed in the Second World War, and it is only now that I can look back and see the damage that loss did to my father and grandparents.

These individual losses were not easily overcome, and the after effects continue long after a generation has disappeared, especially when so many were so young when they were killed.

Commemorative stone for Cecil H. Sewell unveiled in Greenwich in August 2018. (Photo: Brian Aldrich)

Clausewitz famously said that 'War is merely the continuation of policy by other means.' The European nations went into the First World War firmly believing that was the case and that the war would be over by Christmas. Instead millions of individuals died in a conflict which led to no further progress but instead to another equally devastating conflict. And yet, today, if the theatres of war are sufficiently distant, it is easy for us to slip back into thinking Clausewitz was right.

War memorials listing all the individual names of village, town or district are an invention of that generation post 1918, a product of their general revulsion against all-out war involving conscripts and civilians as much as professional military personnel. For a time people were aware of the enormity of what they had allowed to happen and the devastation it has caused, and with the motto 'Never again', they invented the rituals of remembrance which now have been passed downto our generations who have no personal experience of either conflict.

As we look down the lists of names of those lost collected in this book, we need to keep that motto in mind as well to remind us that warfare conducted either near or far away can never merely be the continuation of policy by other means. Everywhere it creates its own reality and devastating consequences.

Introduction

Exactly 100 years after the end of World War One seemed like the right time to publish the Greenwich Roll of Honour. While some memorials have the names of those lost inscribed for all to see, the Greenwich War Memorial had its names deposited inside - almost rendering the fallen invisible.

A copy of the Roll of Honour was originally placed at the Town Hall and then at the Heritage Centre. But in that setting it was an object of occasional reference. This booklet aims to put the names of the fallen into homes, schools and libraries so that "Lest We Forget" becomes something we can truly mean.

In researching the Roll of Honour it became apparent that there were in fact two lists. The Greenwich Borough War Memorial at the top of Maze Hill states on it that it contains a Roll of Honour with over 1600 names and the borough's archives have a list which matches that in size. But a second list, seemingly printed to accompany the Order of Service for the unveiling, is substantially longer. Perhaps produced with less haste than the first, the longer of the two lists has over 240 additions, at least 300 amendments - mostly to regiment names but also surnames and initials - and almost 40 names removed. The revised list has almost 1850 names.

This booklet provides a reproduction of the longer of the two lists. Many names don't list regiments - where they do, abbreviations have been unabbreviated for ease of reading. Where the original list occasionally slipped out of alphabetical order, that has been corrected. The list was compiled by the old Metropolitan Borough of Greenwich which included Greenwich, Charlton, Kidbrooke, and parts of Blackheath and Deptford. However, in the photography section of this booklet, I have acknowledged the current boundaries of the Royal Borough of Greenwich with pictures of war memorials also in SE9 and SE18.

Although I have occasionally referred to the Commonwealth War Graves Commission website to double check facts, I have - with a couple of exceptions - tried not to use external sources to correct any possible errors in order to maintain the integrity of the list.

In addition to the organisations and individuals listed elsewhere who contributed towards the funding of this endeavour, special thanks must go to Barbara Holland, Julian Watson and Mary Mills for their invaluable assistance. Thanks also to the Revd Canon Chris Moody for providing the Foreword.

The booklet provides an opportunity to reflect on the names and the lives of those that died. Hopefully for some it might also be a starting point for further research to learn more about the fallen. For links to additional resources, visit www.greenwich.co.uk/rollofhonour/

Rob Powell, Editor.

The Greenwich Borough War Memorial

As soon as the war ended in 1918, the Borough of Greenwich established a War Memorial Committee to erect a memorial to the many, many hundreds of men from across the borough that had been killed.

At the same time, the council wanted to deal with what was described in one newspaper as a "dangerous corner of the park wall," at the junction of Maze Hill and Charlton Road. In choosing this as the location for the new War Memorial, it allowed both issues to be neatly dealt with.

The road improvement scheme and the memorial were both designed by the Borough Engineer and Surveyor Mr Charles P. Courtenay. The contract for the work was awarded to John Mowlem & Co Ltd. It was reported that the total cost was about £1700, with the memorial paid for by public subscription and the road improvements paid for by the council.

The new memorial was unveiled on 11th November 1922 at 2.30pm. The official unveiling was carried out by Mr Harry Bolton Sewell. Sewell, who lived at 26 Crooms Hill, lost three sons in the war. His eldest son, Cecil Harold Sewell, was posthumously awarded the Victoria Cross. A copy of the Roll of Honour was placed inside a casket by 11 year old Winifred Saunders whose father Lance Corporal Francis Saunders, a local postman, was killed in action. The casket was then deposited inside the new memorial. The inscription on it says:

IN GLORIOUS AND GRATEFUL MEMORY OF THE MEN OF THIS BOROUGH WHO GAVE THEIR LIVES IN THE GREAT WAR. THE NUMBER EXCEEDS 1,600 AND THEIR NAMES ARE RECORDED IN A ROLL OF HONOR [sic] DEPOSITED INSIDE THE MEMORIAL.

On the opposite page are extracts from the Kentish Mercury's report on the unveiling.

GREENWICH HONOURS ITS WAR DEAD

Over 1,600 names on the roll of honour; several thousands of families of Greenwich with their sorrows re-awakened, and their representatives taking part in the only funeral obsequies that they were permitted to attend.

The people began to assemble early in the vicinity of the memorial, which raised itself conspicuously in the breach of the monotonous wall surrounding Greenwich Park at the top of Westcombe Hill.

For an hour or two prior to half past two there had been processions in miniature to the spot. Family parties bearing handsome wreaths, working men carrying handsome tributes, evidently the outcome of collective contribution. Saddest of all, children bearing with rather wondrous expression bunches of flowers expressive of an ever growing realisation that loss will mature as the years go by.

On a small platform in due time appeared the chief actors in this now familiar unveiling drama, or tragedy - the Mayor in his robes and chain of office, Sir Charles Stone, the ex-Mayor, the Bishop of Woolwich in his robes, Mr H.B. Sewell another prominent participator, Captain Sir Ian Hamilton Benn, aldermen, members of the Council, officials, clergy and others.

There was a pause as the band ceased and from the adjacent heath came the murmur of the players at their games.

The Bishop of Woolwich recited the opening sentences of the Burial Service. An almost painful pause ensued, and then came the unveiling - surely as tense a moment that the borough has ever experienced.

Mr Sewell stepped forward, and, in tones that rang out strikingly in the extreme silence, said: "On behalf of the people of Greenwich and in glorious and grateful memory of the men of this borough who gave their lives in the Great War, I unveil this memorial."

All hearts went out to the tiny maiden [Winifred Saunders], hastily wiping the tears from her eyes as she came forward, and all felt the poignancy of the scene - the man who had lost the flower of his family, the child who had lost her parent.

Little Winnie, guided by Mr Sewell, placed, in full view of the spectators, the roll of honour in a leaden casket which was then handed to a workman. A pause ensued whilst the casket was sealed, the "tap tap" of the workman's hammer being the only sound. Then the casket was brought back, exhibited to those present, and handed to the tiny girl, who timidly pushed it into the cavity. Mr Sewell cemented and sealed the aperture and the Bishop dedicated the memorial.

The Greenwich Roll of Honour

A

Abbott, W.F.

Acers, W.B.
Machine Gun Corps

Adam, D.W.
Machine Gun Corps

Adams, A.F.
Bedfordshire Regiment

Adams, A.F.
Royal Army Service Corps

Adams, E.E.
Royal Scots

Adams, J.A.
Royal West Kent Regiment

Adams, W.H.
Royal Army Service Corps

Adkins, C.A.

Adkins, M.
Royal Horse Artillery

Adkinson, G.

Aedy, T.E.
4th Hussars

Aerto, L.
20th London

Aitken, R.W.
Royal West Kent Regiment

Akast, W.
Royal West Kent Regiment

Akers, W.B.
Royal Field Artillery

Alder, W.S.
Coldstream Guards

Aldous, H.G.

Aldrick, F.J.
20th London

Alexander, A.H.
East Kent Regiment

Alford, E.

Algar, H.C.
Royal West Kent Regiment

Allan, W.H.
Royal Garrison Artillery

Allen, C.G.
Royal Garrison Artillery

Allen, S.G.
Royal Field Artillery

Allen, W.G.
3rd London

Allum, G.
HMS Hawke

Amess, W.M.F.
Royal West Kent Regiment

Anderson, A.
6th Staffordshire

Anderson, A.W.
4th London

Anderson, H.T.
King's Royal Rifle Corps

Anderson, J.
Rifle Brigade

Anderson, J.M.C.

Andrews, H.
East Kent Regiment

Andrews, J.
Royal West Kent Regiment

Andrews, S.M.
Army Ordnance Department

Angel, A.
Royal Welsh Fusiliers

Angel, J.M.

Annells, T.
Middlesex Regiment

Apps, E.
Royal Fusiliers

Archer, C.F.
18th London

Archer, G.F.
Royal Field Artillery

Archer, W.
Royal Field Artillery

Archer, W.
2nd Yorkshire

Arnold, C.W.
East Kent Regiment

Arnold, H.
HMS Hogue

Arnott, J.R.
Royal Field Artillery

Arrowsmith, A.J.
Royal Army Medical Corps

Ashby, W.C.
Lancashire Regiment

Ashford, T.W.

Asquith, G.
20th London

Aston, F.B.

Atkinson, G.J.
15th Hussars

Attfield, F.J.
Royal Fusiliers

Attwell, G.A.
Royal Garrison Artillery

Attwell, S.R.
Royal Field Artillery

Austin, D.J.
Royal Field Artillery

Austin, G.W.
26th Hussars

Avery, John
Labour Corps

Ayres, E.
Dorsetshire Regiment

B

Bach, W.

Backhouse, F.
King's Own Yorkshire Light Infantry
MILITARY MEDAL &
DISTINGUISHED
CONDUCT MEDAL

Backhouse, H.
HMS President

Bagg, F.
Royal Fusiliers

Baggett, J.J.
King's Royal Rifle Corps

Bailey, F.
Royal Fusiliers

Baisden, N.A.

Baker, A.
100th Training Reserve Battalion

Baker, C.A.
1st Bedfordshire

Baker, E.J.
HMS Pathfinder

Baker, W.E.J.
1st London

Baldwin, E.H.A.
Canadian Infantry

Baldwin, F.G.
HMS Africa

Baldwin, H.

Baldwin, W.R.

Ballance, L.A.
King's Royal Rifle Corps

Balsom, J.
Royal Field Artillery

Balsom, W.J.

Banks, A.G.
London Scottish

Banks, E.F.

Banks, H.R.W.
23rd London

Bannister, C.R.
Dorsetshire Regiment

Barber, G.B.
17th King's Royal Rifle Corps

Bargin, T.E.

Barham, T.
Rifle Brigade

Barker, J.W.
Royal Army Medical Corps
MILITARY MEDAL

Barkwith, F.E.
Royal West Kent Regiment

Barley, E.
Royal Fusiliers

Barley, G.B.

Barnes, S.W.

Barnett, L de B
Royal West Kent Regiment

Barr, G.
Rifle Brigade

Barrett, A.
20th London

Barrett, A.J.
East Kent Regiment

Barrow, C.G.
20th London

Barrow, J.S.
Royal Army Service Corps

Barrow, R.H.
Royal Warwickshire Regiment

Barry, T.A.
Royal West Kent Regiment

Bartholomew, H.

Bartholomew, T.
SS Ansconia

Bartlett, A.S.
Australian Light Horse

Bartley, A.J.
East Kent Regiment

Barton, R.E.
1st Royal Fusiliers

Bartram, S.J.
HMS Latona

Baskett, A.C.
East Surrey Regiment

Baskett, G.O.
1st / 2nd London Regiment

Bass, H.C.

Bass, W.C.

Batchford, A.J.
London Regiment

Bateman, F.G.
Royal Flying Corps

Bateman, J.H.
1st Manchesters

Bates, F.

Baulsom, G.
HMS Hyacinth

Baulsom, H.
Royal Field Artillery

Baulsom, J.T.
Royal Field Artillery

Baulsom, R.
East Kent Regiment

Baxter, A.

Baxter, W.J. (Jnr)

Baxter, W.J. (Snr)

Bayfield, S.B.
20th London

Beach, J.M.
18th London

Beak, W.G.
London Regiment

Beal, F.
Royal Army Service Corps

Beames, E.R.
Grenadier Guards

Beard, G.
East Kent Regiment

Beasley, R.
Royal Field Artillery

Beauchamp, W.
Royal West Surrey Regiment

Beaver, P.G.

Beckenham, H.W.

Beckett, G.Z.
North Lancashire Regiment

Beckford, F.
20th London

Beech, W.
7th King's Royal Rifle Corps

Beeney, W.E.A.
20th London

Beer, G.R.
20th London

Belchin, F.H.
Royal Fusiliers

Bell, W.J.
Canadian Infantry

Belton, H.

Belton, H.G.
1st Surrey Rifles

Bennett, E.
Royal Army Service Corps

Bennett, E.T.
10th Middlesex

Bennett, J.H.
Middlesex Regiment

Bennett, W.
Royal West Kent Regiment

Bennett, W.
Royal Field Artillery

Bennison, A.
20th London

Benstead, F.
3rd Essex

Berry, C.

Berry, C.J.
King's Royal Rifle Corps

Berry, F.P.
20th London

Berry, J.
Rifle Brigade

Betts, J.
Royal West Kent Regiment

Bevis, H.
20th London

Bew, S.J.
2nd Royal Fusiliers

Beyant, A.G.

Billingsley, F.W.
1st London

8

Binfield, C.
Australian Imperial Force

Binning, A.
14th London Scottish

Birch, J.

Bird, C.H.
4th Gordon Highlanders

Biscoe, A.J.
Royal Irish Rifles

Bishop, F.

Bishop, F.A.
23rd London

Black, G.W.
Royal Field Artillery

Black, H.J.
HMS Simson

Blackman, W.J.

Blackmore, W.J.
Royal Army Service Corps

Blatcher, A.E.

Bloomfield, J.R.
Essex Regiment

Blows, H.J.
6th London

Boater, H.

Bobey, G.W.
Royal Field Artillery

Bobey, S.
2nd London

Bolt, G.R.

Bonds, G.

Booker, H.G.
Royal Fusiliers

Bosanquet, S.C.
Middlesex Regiment

Bostock, J.
HMS Turbulent

Boswell, G.
London Regiment

Bosworth, A.

Boult, G.

Boulton, F.E.
6th City of London

Bouzer, J.A.

Bowen, W.C.
East Kent Regiment

Bowers, F.

Bowers, F.E.
Somerset Light Infantry

Bowers, J.A.
Royal Engineers

Bowers, J.A.
Munster Fusiliers

Bowie, H.

Bowring, L.B.
Lancashire Fusiliers

Bowring, L.C.

Boyce, J.W.
Royal Garrison Artillery

Brackell, W.H.
Royal Army Medical Corps

Bradbury, W.J.
20th London

Bradford, A.E.
Rifle Brigade

Bradford, G.
King's Royal Rifle Corps

Bradley, W.A.
Royal Sussex Regiment

Bradshaw, E.
Middlesex Regiment

Brand, P.C.
21st London

Brant, F.E.
3rd/20th London

Brant, W.
Royal Berkshire Regiment

Brawn, T.E.
Australian Imperial Force

Bray, E.L.

Breacker, J.W.

Breed, A.
London Regiment

Breed, E.
Royal Fusiliers

Breman, R.

Brennan, F.
20th London

Brennan, R.
Royal Field Artillery

Brewer, J.A.
Rifle Brigade

Brigden, A.T.
Royal Army Service Corps

Briggs, A.
London Regiment

Brightwell, J.W.
HMS Africa

Brindley, T.
Royal Army Service Corps

Bristow, S.L.

Bromley, E.T.
Machine Gun Corps

Brooker, T.E.

Brooks, E.T.
15th London

Brooks, L.
10th East Kent

Brown, A.J.
8th Royal Sussex

Brown, C.E.
20th London

Brown, C.S.
Canadian Expeditionary Force

Brown, F.
Royal West Kent Regiment

Brown, S.
King's Royal Rifle Corps

Brown, S.V.
Royal Garrison Artillery

Brown, W.J.J.

Brown, W.T.
19th London

Browning, A.
Royal Field Artillery

Brunning, C.J.
20th London

Bryan, T.W.

Bryant, A.G.
Rifle Brigade

Bryant, C.
Royal Army Service Corps

Bryant, D.

Bryant, F.E.
20th London

Bryant, G.A.
Rifle Brigade

Bryant, W.H.
Royal West Kent Regiment

Buckell, J.H.
20th London

Buckingham, A.
Royal Field Artillery

Buckingham, A.E.
Royal Field Artillery

Buckland, J.

Buckle, H.W.
HMS Good Hope

Buff, R.
Durham Light Infantry

Buffs, G.

Bugg, G.
1st London

Buhl, W.H.
20th London

Bullock, G.H.

Bullock, H.C.

Bumpus, B.E.
Northumberland Fusiliers

Bunt, C.R.T.

Burgess, C.L.A.H.
2nd Wiltshire

Burgess, F.D.
King's Royal Rifle Corps

Burgiss, W.W.
Royal Engineers

Burn, H.G.

Burness, H.W.

Burrell, C.
Royal Field Artillery

Burrell, E.G.
Shropshire Light Infantry

Burrell, P.

Burrell, W.
2nd Royal West Kent

Burrows, J.W.
Royal Fusiliers

Burrows, V.J.
Royal West Kent Regiment

Bush, C.G.
Royal Army Service Corps

Bush, W.J.
20th London

Bussey, C.
20th London

Butler, H.
Royal West Kent Regiment

Butler, W.

Butler, W.T.
Labour Corps

Byrne, G.
Royal Fusiliers

C

Cadmore, A.C.

Cailes, A.E.
Norfolk Regiment

Cairns, J.A.C.
King's Own Scottish Borderers

Callagham, D.
Royal Garrison Artillery

Calligari, J.J.
Royal Army Ordnance Corps

Calloway, C.
Royal West Kent Regiment

Canelle, E.E.
Royal Fusiliers

Carden, W.

Carey, J.
HMS Yarmouth

Carey, M.
16th Cameronians

Carpenter, W.
11th Hussars

Carr, V.F.
Royal Garrison Artillery

Carretta, A.
Royal Army Medical Corps

Carroll, J.C.

Carter, A.
Royal Fusiliers

Carter, C.J.
20th London

Carter, E.W.
Middlesex Regiment

Carter, G.A.
13th Dragoons

Carter, H.
Royal Army Service Corps

Carter, J.T.
East Kent Regiment

Cartwright, H.C.

Cassidy, J.

Cassidy, W.

Catherine, G.L.
Northumberland Fusiliers

Cawnden, S.A.
46th Training Reserve Battalion

Cawte, R.S.
Middlesex Regiment

Chadwick, T.

Chambers, A.E.
Royal West Kent Regiment

Chambers, J.W.H.
HMS Curacoa

Chance, H.
6th London Rifles

Chaplin, T.S.
Royal Engineers

Chapman, C.W.

Chapman, G.
Rifle Brigade

Chapman, H.W.
Royal West Kent Regiment

Chapman, T.

Chappell, A.I.

Charlton, F.T.
South Lancashire Regiment

Chatfield, J.

Cheeseman, A.R.

Cheeseman, T.

Cheeseman, T.G.
Royal West Kent Regiment

Cheetham, A.
Royal West Kent Regiment

Chesmon, A.W.

Chetter, H.
Grenadier Guards

Chidgey, A.
Royal Navy

Chilcott, W.J.
Royal Field Artillery

Chilvers, W.W.
Royal West Kent Regiment

Chismon, A.W.
Rifle Brigade

Christain, R.
Royal Field Artillery

Christer, G.D.
Royal Garrison Artillery

Chubb, H.W.
HMS Raglan

Church, J.
Royal West Kent Regiment

Churcher, A.H.
East Surrey Regiment

Churchill, A.E.

Churchill, W.G.
HMS Mosquito

Clare, A.B.
Rifle Brigade

Clark, G.
2nd London

Clark, H.G.
Royal Garrison Artillery

Clark, H.T.C.
Middlesex Regiment

Clark, S.C.
2nd Scots Guards

Clark, V.R.

Clark, W.T.
Royal West Kent Regiment

Clark, W.W.
Royal Field Artillery

Clarke, C.H.

Clay, W.T.
Royal Field Artillery

Claydon, F.

Claydon, F.W.
HMS Arion

Clayton, J.H.
Royal Army Medical Corps

Clements, D.F.
19th London

Clements, N.F.J.
HMS Courageous

Clements, W.C.
Rifle Brigade

Clery, N.C.
Royal Field Artillery

Clifforth, H.J.

Clifforth, T.G.
Royal Engineers

Clifton, H.A.
East Lancashire Regiment

Clifton, J.H.W.
London Regiment

Coates, W.J.
HMS Vanguard

Cobb, T.G.H.
Sherwood Foresters

Cockett, W.G.

Coddington, C.J.
Wiltshire Regiment

Coddington, W.J.
Rifle Brigade

Coe, F.W.

Cohen, A.

Cohen, H.
East Kent Regiment

Coker, W.G.
Grenadier Guards

Colberry, A.E.
Honourable Artillery Company

Colcutt, T.M.
Gloucestershire Regiment

Cole, J.
Royal West Surrey Regiment

Cole, W.G.
Suffolk Regiment

Coleman, A.
Royal Garrison Artillery

Coleman, R.
Royal Fusiliers

Coleman, R.N.

Coles, G.

Coles, G.E.
Rifle Brigade

Coles, J.
14th Rifle Brigade

Coley, F.C.

Collett, R.

Collett, T.E.
3rd Middlesex

Collins, H.W.
HMS Invincible

Collins, M.

Collins, R.H.
6th London Rifles

Cook, E.R.

Cook, F.R.
East Yorkshire Regiment

Cook, H.J.
East Kent Regiment

Cook, H.R.

Cook, J.W.
20th London

Coombe, A.W.H.
Royal Engineers

Coombe, C.
Royal Engineers

Coomber, R.

Cooney, C.W.
Royal Field Artillery

Cooper, F.E.

Cooper, J.
Royal Army Ordnance Corps

Cooper, J.F.
19th Yorkshire

Cooper, J.S.
20th London

Cooper, N.W.
HMS Kent

Cooper, S.

Cooper, W.A.L.

Cornelius, J.R.
Royal Field Artillery

Cornell, A.
King's Royal Rifle Corps

Cornell, H.

Coster, A.E.
2nd Border

Coster, A.T.
2nd Border

Coster, G.
London Regiment

Coster, R.
2nd Border

Coster, S.R.

Coster, T.A.

Cottam, H.F.
HMS Aboukir

Cowen, F.A.
4th Middlesex

Cowen, H.
East Kent Regiment

Cowland, J.T.
13th London

Cowley, A.E.
Royal Garrison Artillery

Cowley, W.G.
Royal Field Artillery

Cownden, L.A.
Royal West Kent Regiment
MILITARY MEDAL

Cox, T.
Rifle Brigade

Crage, J.
Royal Field Artillery

Crandon, L.A.
Northumberland Fusiliers

Crane, C.A.

Cranfield, W.
HMS Rhododendron

Crawford, A.G.

Crawford, J.R.
Grenadier Guards

Crawley, E.J.
20th London

Creagh, O.C.
Royal Field Artillery

Creck, C.L.
8th London

Creeden, J.
West India Regiment

Crick, C.C.
15th London

Cripps, G.
HMS Aboukir

Cripps, H.G.
22nd Northumberland Fusiliers

Crisp, W.
Royal West Kent Regiment

Crompton, P.
21st London

Crompton, P.A.
Royal Sussex Regiment

Crook, H.
Middlesex Regiment

Crouch, E.C.

Crouch, J.A.
York & Lancaster Regiment

Crow, N.T.
King's Royal Rifle Corps

Crow, W.F.
HMS Shark

Crowther, J.
Middlesex Regiment

Cullem, P.A.

Cummings, W.
Lancashire Fusiliers

Curran, F.L.
Royal Horse Artillery

Curren, O.
20th London

Cust, R.

Cwiness, F.G.
East Kent Regiment

D

Dabin, R.E.
20th London

Dacey, J.
Rifle Brigade

Daley, F.A.
Royal Army Service Corps

Daley, R.
Royal West Surrey Regiment

Dallimore, H.J.
Royal Field Artillery

Daly, W.G.
Royal West Kent Regiment

Daniel, A.A.
Rifle Brigade

Daniells, J.
Middlesex Regiment

Daniels, E.
London Regiment

Daniels, J.G.
155th Company Labour Corps

Daniels, P.

Daniels, R.
East Kent Regiment

Daniels, W.E.
46th Training Reserve Battalion

Daniels, W.J.
Royal West Surrey Regiment

Darbon, D.

Daries, A.

Dauncey, F.
Royal Army Service Corps

Davey, C.
SS Heron

Davies, A.W.
Royal Field Artillery

Davies, C.E.
King's Royal Rifle Corps

Davies, H.

Davis, H.
20th London

Davis, H.G.
Norfolk Regiment

Davis, W.N.
Warwickshire Regiment

Davison, C.F.
HMS Cressy

Davison, W.
West Yorkshire Regiment

Davy, B.J.
Naval Volunteer Reserve

Dawe, C.W.
12th London

Dawe, G.W.
Royal Marine Light Infantry

Dawes, C.J.
20th London

Dawes, T.H.
Brigade of Guards

Day, C.
5th Royal Sussex

Dealy, J.A.
Royal Engineers

Delaney, A.S.
6th Northamptonshire

Dell, W.L.

Dellow, L.C.

Delmege, C.P.

Denham, J.
ss Kaffir Prince

Denine, J.
2nd Machine Gun Corps

Dennard, W.H.

Dennis, H.A.
Royal Engineers

Dent, C.F.
Rifle Brigade

Dent, J.R.
Rifle Brigade

Denton, A.
20th London

Devine, D.W.
Rifle Brigade

Devitt, W.G.C.
1st London

Devonshire, J.W.

Devonshire, T.

Dew, W.C.
Honourable Artillery Company

Dickerson, A.
20th London

Dickerson, C.H.
Argyll & Sutherland Highlanders

Dickson, A.C.
Royal Army Medical Corps

Diett, J.
Royal Field Artillery

Diggins, C.W.
20th London

Dilks, H.
Royal West Kent Regiment
MILITARY MEDAL

Dillon, G.F.
HMS Lancaster

Dimmock, E.
Royal West Kent Regiment

Dimmock, F.
Royal West Kent Regiment

Dimmock, W.G.
London Regiment

Dinwiddy, C.H.
Royal Field Artillery

Diplock, J.H.
10th London

Dippie, K.

Disbray, W.H.
20th London

Divers, W.
Canadian Imperial Force

Divers, W.C.
Royal West Kent Regiment

Divitt, W.G.

Diwell, G.C.
HMS Vanguard

Dixon, F.
Royal Engineers

Dixon, F.B.
Royal Engineers

Dobin, R.E.

Dolden, H.C.
Royal West Kent Regiment

Dolden, L.C.
2nd Royal Warwickshire

Dolphin, J.S.
HMS Cressy

Dolphin, V.O.
Royal Field Artillery

Dolphin, W.
HMS Natal

Dolson, T.C.
King's Royal Rifle Corps

Donoghue, R.O.

Dougal, G.W.

Douglas, A.
14th London Scottish

Dowdall, F.
Royal West Kent Regiment

Dowell, S.H.
London Rifle Brigade

Down, H.V.
Rifle Brigade

Downie, W.K.
Royal Garrison Artillery

Downs, A.
18th London

Dowse, C.
King's Royal Rifle Corps

Dowsing, A.C.
Northamptonshire Regiment

Drain, S.H.

Drake, A.
17th King's Royal Rifle Corps

Driscoll, F.J.
Royal Army Service Corps

Driver, A.O.

Dryden, G.W.

Duce, A.B.

Duce, A.J.

Duggan, F.J.

Duggan, P.W.

Dumpley, M.F.
17th Machine Gun Corps

Duncan, W.

Dunn, R.
Machine Gun Corps

Durbridge, J.P.T.

Durrant, F.A.
Royal Field Artillery

Durrant, G.

Duttfield, A.
Royal West Kent Regiment

Duttfield, T.
HMS Hawke

Dyer, C.
Royal Navy

Dyer, C.E.
Royal Marine Light Infantry

Dyer, R.G.

E

Eager, G.L.
15th London

Eagles, A.
Royal Scots

Earle, W.M.

Earley, G.T.
10th Royal West Kent

Earley, R.
SS Heron

Ede-Harris, J.

Edey, W.J.

Edge, W.H.

Edmonds, H.W.
Royal Horse Artillery

Edwards, C.

Edwards, C.V.G.
Royal Sussex Regiment

Edwards, E.W.
Royal West Surrey Regiment

Edwards, F.C.
Rifle Brigade

Edwards, G.
Royal West Surrey Regiment

Edwards, G.T.
King's Royal Rifle Corps

Edwards, J.S.
King's Royal Rifle Corps

Edwards, R.C.
King's Royal Rifle Corps

Eicke, O.M.
Royal Field Artillery

Eldbridge, J.E.
Royal Army Ordnance Corps

Eldered, M.

Elgar, W.C.

Elleston, W.
13th King's Royal Rifles

Ellis, T.E.
20th London

Elphick, E.W.

Elpluck, A.

Emlin, E.J.
Royal Garrison Artillery

Endean, F.E.
Royal Irish Rifles

Enerson, H.G.

Entwistle, F.
Norfolk Regiment

Essenhigh, C.E.M.
Royal Garrison Artillery

Eveleigh, A.E.
20th London

Everett, E.A.
HMS Recruit

Everett, J.G.
HMS Euryalus

Everson, H.
20th London

Everson, H.G.
Royal Field Artillery

F

Fairlie, W.
Royal Garrison Artillery

Fairman, C.

Fairman, S.C.
Devonshire Regiment

Faithful, A.E.

Faithful, E.
Royal West Surrey Regiment

Faithful, E.C.
Royal Fusiliers

Farrant, E.E.

Farrant, J.E.
Royal Sussex Regiment

Farrin, A.H.
Royal Sussex Regiment

Faulkener, W.W.
East Kent Regiment

Faulkner, A.G.
1st Border

Fayers, E.

Fearn, A.

Fearn, S.

Felton, H.W.

Fiddler, J.F.

Fidgett, B.
Royal Army Service Corps

Finch, E.T.
Royal Field Artillery

Finch, H.A.
Rifle Brigade

Finch, S.
9th Lancers

Finch, W.M.

Fincham, A.M.
20th London

Finlay, J.R.
HMS Botha

Fisher, A.G.
Royal West Surrey Regiment

Fisher, F.G.
10th Essex

Fisher, R.A.
17th London

Fisher, W.R.

Fitzgerald, W.
Royal Naval Transport Service

Flanders, T.W.

Fletcher, D.

Flint, J.E.
Royal Scots

Florence, H.B.

Forbes, G.A.
4th London

Forbes, R.A.
London Scottish

Forbes, W.G.A.

Fordham, H.
13th London

Foss, T.
Inniskillin Fusiliers

Foucar, J.L.
12th London

Foulds, J.
London Regiment

Fowler, E.
York & Lancaster Regiment

Fowler, J.

Fowler, N.

Fowler, T.

Fox, D.C.
28th London

Fox, H.
5th South Lancashire

Francis, A.E.
East Surrey Regiment

Francis, W.G.
Royal Air Force

Franklin, H.

Franklin, R.A.
Bedfordshire Regiment

Franks, W.H.

Fraser, T.
24th London

Fraser, W.
Canadian Imperial Force

Frazier, W.F.

Freeman, A.
1st Border

Freeman, D.
Middlesex Regiment

Freemantle, D.J.
2nd Dorsetshire

Freer, J.
Labour Corps

French, A.
East Kent Regiment

French, F.C.

French, J.
Royal Fusiliers

French, R.
London Regiment

French, W.R.

French, W.S.A.
3rd Royal Sussex

Fricker, A.E.
18th London

Friday, H.J.
20th London

Friday, W.G.
20th London

Frost, G.T.
7th London

Frostick, J.W.
Rifle Brigade

Fry, J.
1st Coldstream Guards

Fryer, A.
Royal West Kent Regiment

Fryer, T.
Royal West Kent Regiment

Fudge, T.
Northamptonshire Regiment

Fudge, W.H.
King's Royal Rifle Corps

Funnell, A.
1st London

Furner, E.
4th East Surrey

G

Gadsen, W.
Rifle Brigade

Gale, R.H.
8th Essex Cyclist Regiment

Gallagher, J.M.
20th London

Galley, A.
Royal Fusiliers

Gambling, A.
Royal Fusiliers

Gambling, A.A.
Royal Fusiliers

Gandy, H.
East Kent Regiment

Garland, H.

Garratt, L.
20th London

Garrett, A.G.
Royal Fusiliers

Garrett, R.S.
Rifle Brigade

Garton, E.A.
5th London

Gaster, E.

Gaster, P.S.
Royal Air Force

Gatehouse, F.
Northumberland Fusiliers

Gatehouse, M.L.
East Kent Regiment

Gear, T.W.
Royal Army Service Corps

George, J.E.
East Kent Regiment

George, T.
East Kent Regiment

Germain, G.F.
6th London

Gibbon, C.
Royal Field Artillery

Gibbs, A.H.
20th London

Gibbs, G.R.
5th Dragoons

Gibbs, J.T.
Royal West Kent Regiment

Gibson, C.
Royal Horse Artillery

Gibson, T.
Australian Imperial Force

Gilbert, R.C.
HMTS Booda A30

Gilbrain, F.W.
Middlesex Regiment

Giles, A.L.
19th London

Giles, F.A.

Gilham, J.T.
20th London

Gill, F.W.
4th East Surrey

Gill, W.T.

Gillman, H.

Gilroy, J.J.
Royal Army Medical Corps

Gjems, A.O.M.
5th Royal Fusiliers

Glass, F.
20th London

Glassborrow, T.G.

Goad, W.F.T.
6th East Kent

Gobbett, F.
East Yorkshire Regiment

Goble, W.A.
Royal Garrison Artillery

Goddard, A.H.
Royal Army Medical Corps

Goddard, C.F.
20th London

Godfrey, W.A.

Golding, F.S.

Golding, H.G.
Middlesex Regiment

Golding, W.I.
5th Canadian Brigade

Goldsmith, G.
Royal West Kent Regiment

Goldsmith, W.C.
Royal West Kent Regiment

Golle, C.V.
London Regiment

Gomer, F.
28th London

Gomer, P.
Worcestershire Regiment

Goodbody, F.

Goodlad, F.J.
Royal West Kent Regiment

Goodman, W.
Royal West Kent Regiment

Goodwin, G.

Goodwin, H.F.P.
20th London

Goodyer, N.B.

Goodyer, W.B.
West Yorkshire Regiment

Gore, G.B.

Goslin, E.W.

Gowland, B.
*Duke of Cornwall's Light
Infantry*

Gratten, A.
Australian Imperial Force

Gray, E.J.
Royal Army Medical Corps

Greathead, A.
Royal Air Force

Green, C.
47th Training Reserve Battalion

Green, C.G.
East Surrey Regiment

Green, J.H.

Greenhill, W.

Greig, A.
Seaforth Highlanders

Grice, A.R.

Griffin, A.

Griffin, E.
Royal Dublin Fusiliers

Griffiths, A.E.
20th London

Griffiths, F.J.
4th London

Griffiths, H.E.
7th Essex

Grounbudge, W.A.

Groves, E.C.
London Regiment

Groves, R.H.
3rd London FA

Groves, S.J.
Royal Horse Artillery

Guess, E.C.
20th London

Gull, W.
7th East Yorkshire

H

Hackney, C.J.
Royal Air Force

Haddon, E.H.
119th Infantry Indian Army

Haining, W.C.
Royal Air Force

Hair, E.

Hake, A.J.
Royal Sussex Regiment

Hale, M.
Royal Garrison Artillery

Hall, C.G.
Middlesex Regiment

Halliday, S.L.
HMS Lark

Hamer, W.R.
London Regiment
MILITARY MEDAL

Hamilton, E.

Hamilton, E.L.
2nd Border

Hamp, J.

Hamp, J.C.
Royal Engineers

Hancock, E.

Hankins, H.
Royal Engineers

Hankins, J.W.C.

Hankins, P.
Royal Army Ordnance Corps

Hanley, W.J.T.

Hannam, G.T.

Hannen, T.J.
8th Royal West Kent

Harding, C.
King's African Rifles

Harding, R.G.
1st London

Harding, W.
Royal West Kent Regiment

Hardwell, G.
21st King's Royal Rifle Corps

Hardy, H.

Hardy, J.F.

Hardy, R.
Grenadier Guards

Hare, R.
2nd King's Royal Rifle Corps

Harford, W.
East Kent Regiment

Harler, W.J.
Rifle Brigade

Harrell, W.J.
Rifle Brigade

Harris, A.E.
Royal Army Service Corps

Harris, B.D.
Royal Fusiliers

Harris, C.A.
Royal West Kent Regiment

Harris, C.N.
7th Middlesex

Harris, E.J.
Royal West Kent Regiment

Harris, H.C.
Royal West Kent Regiment

Harris, H.G.
Royal West Kent Regiment

Harris, J.A.E.
Royal Field Artillery

Harris, T.

Hart, A.

Hart, A.R.
Royal Horse Artillery

Hart, W.
Rifle Brigade

Harvie, P.J.
Royal Army Veterinary Corps

Harwood, A.
Royal Army Medical Corps

Harwood, R.E.
20th London

Harwood, W.H.
HMS Astraea

Hattimore, F.
Royal Horse Artillery

Hawker, A.J.
Duke of Cornwall's Light Infantry

Hawkins, A.
Royal Sussex Regiment

Hawkins, A.W.
11th Royal Sussex

Hawkins, H.

Hawkins, P.

Hawkins, R.T.
10th Royal Sussex

Hayden, C.
Grenadier Guards

Hayden, W.C.
Grenadier Guards

Hayes, C.
King's Royal Rifle Corps

Hayes, F.C.
HMS Maidstone

Hayes, T.H.
17th Middlesex

Hayward, G.H.
19th London

Haywood, A.

Haywood, F.F.

Haywood, F.G.
Royal West Kent Regiment

Hazell, S.E.B.
8th Norfolks

Head, D.J.
Essex Regiment

Head, E.A.
HMS Black Prince

Heard, H.

Hearn, H.
11th London

Heasman, G.W.
Royal Field Artillery

Hedges, S.

Henderson, W.

Hendon, D.G.

Hendon, O.G.
20th London

Hendrick, T.H.
Royal Army Pay Corps

Herbert, C.
Royal Air Force

Hesketh, G.T.
20th London

Hewitt, R.
HMS Hogue

Hewlett, W.A.

Hierons, H.P.
9th Lancers

Higgett, F.
17th London

Higgins, J.
Rifle Brigade

Higgitt, R.
20th London

Higham, J.W.
2nd Brigade Canadian

Hill, F.
Military Mounted Police

Hill, G.
Royal West Kent Regiment

Hill, G.E.
HMS Hood

Hill, H.C.
Middlesex Regiment

Hillary, F.T.
Royal Sussex Regiment

Hills, E.
Royal West Kent Regiment

Hinch, J.

Hinnes, E.

Hinson, A.W.
Royal Naval Division

Hinves, A.E.
HMS Cressy

Hinves, A.H.
Coldstream Guards

Hipsey, W.R.
Royal Field Artillery

Hiscock, A.

Hiscock, A.E.
Royal Field Artillery

Hiscock, B.

Hitchcock, C.E.
9th London

Hither, H.G.
3rd London

Hoare, J.
20th London

Hobbs, C.W.
Royal Field Artillery

Hobbs, E.A.
Royal Field Artillery

Hobles, C.W.

Hobles, E.A.

Hodgkinson, H.G.
*Duke of Wellington's Regiment
(West Riding)*

Hodgson, J.S.
20th London

Hogden, W.C.
Royal West Kent Regiment

Holden, G.E.
Royal West Kent Regiment

Holdsworth, A.
HMS Hogue

Hole, J.

Hole, J.A.C.
ss Pollonea

Holford, A.F.
HMS Cressy

Holland, A.E.
Rifle Brigade

Holland, A.H.
Rifle Brigade

Holland, F.F.
HMS Vanguard

Holland, J.L.

Holland, S.F.
HMS Pembroke

Hollidge, J.J.T.
HMS Vanguard

Holloway, G.W.
Royal West Surrey Regiment

Holloway, W.G.

Holman, J.A.
1st London

Holmes, R.H.
7th Royal West Kent

Homewood, A.W.
Royal Horse Artillery

Honey, H.
2nd Royal West Kent

Hopper, V.C.
HMS Mallard

Hopper, W.C.
HMS Strongbow

Hopson, W.W.
*Duke of Cornwall's Light
Infantry*

Horam, W.H.S.
20th London

Horlock, A.I.W.
31st London

Horn, C.

Horne, W.

Horner, A.V.H.
2nd London

Horrell, L.W.

Horrell, T.W.
HMS Hogue

Horsley, W.H.
Royal West Kent Regiment

House, W.S.
12th Middlesex

Howard, W.G.
9th Dorsetshire Regiment

Howe, C.
Royal Fusiliers

Howes, J.
HMS Fearless

Howlett, C.

Hubbard, J.T.
Oxfordshire & Buckinghamshire Light Infantry

Huddlestone, L.G.
Royal Naval Air Service

Hudson, A.T.R.
Durham Light Infantry

Hughes, F.

Hughes, F.T.

Hughes, F.W.
Rifle Brigade

Hughes, J.L.
Royal Field Artillery

Hughes, W.M.H.
9th Welsh Regiment

Hulford, S.A.
HMS Foyle

Hulford, W.C.
1st Royal Bucks

Hulks, R.A.
Royal Fusiliers

Hulme, J.W.
Royal West Kent Regiment

Humphreys, A.W.
HMS Myosotis

Humphreys, E.
Royal Sussex Regiment

Hunt, A.
20th London

Hunt, Bland S. E. De Vere
Royal Artillery

Hunt, G.
London Regiment

Hunt, H.C.
HMS Triumph

Hurren, W.H.
Middlesex Regiment

Hurst, E.B.
Honourable Artillery Company

Huskinson, C.R.

Huskinson, F.J.

Hussey, E.J.
King's Borderers

Hussey, E.T.
Royal Fusiliers

Hutchins, G.
Royal Field Artillery

Hutchins, H.
1st Suffolk

Hutchinson, F.F.
East Kent Regiment

Hutchinson, W.S.
HMS Invincible

Hyde, O.C.B.

I

Indge, A.C.
Royal West Kent Regiment

Indge, F.T.
Royal West Kent Regiment

Ingles, D.
Royal Navy, Chatham Barracks

Insted, W.G.
Rifle Brigade

Ireson, E.J.

Isaac, G.D.
Royal Garrison Artillery

Isaacs, F.J.
Gordon Highlanders

J

Jacklin, J.T.

Jackson, A.G.
13th London

Jackson, A.G.
No 1 Cavalry Cadet School

Jackson, C.T.

Jackson, W.
19th Hussars

Jacobs, A.W.
Royal Fusiliers

Jacobs, W.H.
Royal Navy

Jago, G.F.
Royal Army Service Corps

James, A.
Brigade of Guards

James, R.
Royal Army Medical Corps

James, R.J.
20th London

James, W.G.
10th Middlesex

Janes, W.
Royal Field Artillery

Japp, N.
20th London

Jefferies, A.L.
Royal Naval Air Service

Jefferies, B.

Jeffery, H.
4th York & Lancaster

Jeffery, H.T.

Jeffrey, F.A.
Rifle Brigade

Jeffs, H.W.
20th London

Jehu, D.R.
Royal Army Service Corps

Jelf, H.J.
East Surrey Regiment

Jenkins, G.S.

Jenkins, W.
HMS Good Hope

Jenner, F.W.
Royal Engineers

Jenner, H.G.
London Regiment

Jennings, F.W.
Royal West Kent Regiment

Jennings, N.
10th London

Jessop, A.

Jessup, A.M.
Royal West Kent Regiment

Jewell, C.W.
22nd London

Jobbins, J.E.
Royal West Kent Regiment

Jobbins, T.A.

Johnson, F.W.
West Yorkshire Regiment

Johnson, R.M.
Bedfordshire Regiment

Johnson, W.G.

Jones, A.W.G.
Royal West Kent Regiment

Jones, B.J.
2nd Essex

Jones, G.
8th Gloucestershire

Jones, G.H.
Royal Field Artillery

Jones, H.G.
Royal West Kent Regiment

Jones, J.
2nd London

Jones, J.H.
Royal Irish

Jones, T.

Jones, W.
Royal Army Service Corps

Jordan, A.H.
Royal Garrison Artillery

Jourdin, C.E.
North Lancashire Regiment
DISTINGUISHED
SERVICE ORDER

Joyce, J.
Royal Fusiliers

Jukes, A.W.

Julius, A.E.
Royal Engineers

Juniper, C.W.H.
Essex Regiment

Jupp, G.
HMS Good Hope

K

Kane, T.
4th London

Keeble, T.W.
7th Northumberland Fusiliers

Keeler, W.

Keen, J.H.
Canadian Forces

Keen, W.
King's Royal Rifle Corps

Kellcher, E.
Devonshire Regiment

Kelley, F.T.
Royal Air Force

Kelly, H.J.
King's Royal Rifle Corps

Kemp, A.F.
19th London

Kemp, A.H.
21st London

Kemp, F.

Kemp, G.H.

Kemp, J.
Royal Field Artillery

Kendall, L.F.W.A.
Norfolkshire Regiment

Kendrick, T.H.
Royal Field Artillery

Kennaird, A.J.
Gordon Highlanders

Kennaird, W.F.

Kennard, A.J.
Gordon Highlanders

Kerr, C.
Middlesex Regiment

Kerr, S.R.C.
Royal Field Artillery

Kerr, W.C.R.
Royal Field Artillery

Kerridge, G.
Royal Field Artillery

Kerslake, S.E.
4th East Kent Regiment

Kerstein, C.W.B.

Kerswell, C.J.

Kerswell, H.J.

Kettle, J.T.
Royal Field Artillery

Keys, S.

Kicks, W.
London Regiment

Kilby, H.
MILITARY MEDAL

Kilby, H.H.
Royal Army Service Corps

Killick, A.H.

King, C.
Royal Field Artillery

King, F.
2nd Royal Fusiliers

King, R.
Royal Scots Fusiliers

King, T.E.
Middlesex Regiment

King, T.J.
HMS Mary Rose

Kingscott, W.H.

Kington, A.
17th Middlesex

Kington, A.
Royal Garrison Artillery

Kite, H.E.
Royal Irish

Kither, H.G.
3rd City of London

Kitson, E.G.T.
Duke of Cornwall's Light Infantry

Kittingham, A.R.
20th London

Klee, A.M.

Klein, A.L.
7th Essex

Knapp, A.H.
15th London

Knapp, R.S.
Royal Garrison Artillery

Knight, A.A.
17th London

Knight, J.
Royal Engineers

Knight, J.
East Kent Regiment

Knowles, A.
Royal Field Artillery

Kyle, F.
Australian Imperial Force

Kyle, T.
4th London

L

Lacey, J.
Machine Gun Corps

Ladbury, A.E.
East Surrey Regiment

Ladbury, W.
Royal West Kent Regiment

Laird, A.H.
HMS Hazel

Laite, J.F.

Lake, T.A.
6th Sherwood Foresters

Lamber, D.

Lambert, P.

Lambourne, E.
2nd London

Laming, F.A.
22nd London

Lamkin, J.
HMS Victorious

Lancaster, F.G.

Lancaster, F.H.
20th London

Lancester, H.J.
Royal Field Artillery

Lancy, N.
4th London

Lang, S.D.
*Oxfordshire & Buckinghamshire
Light Infantry*

Langdon, F.J.

Langler, B.M.C.

Langler, J.
Royal Field Artillery

Lanigan, W.
Royal Navy

Lankford,

Lankin, E.J.
Royal Berks Regiment

Larger, H.
5th London

Larkin, E.
Royal West Kent Regiment

Larkin, R.J.A.
Royal West Surrey Regiment

Larking, E.T.

Larking, R.F.

Lawler, D.F.
Royal Fusiliers

Lawrence, F.

Lawrence, H.G.
Royal Field Artillery

Lawrence, T.
Royal West Kent Regiment

Lawrence, W.J.
Royal Army Service Corps

Laycock, F.M.

Lee, E.F.

Lee, H.H.
20th London

Lee, R.

Leeves, E.H.
East Kent Regiment

Lenett, C.

Lengham, W.

Lentchford, A.S.
19th London

Letchford, G.
Grenadier Guards

Levett, C.
Royal West Kent Regiment

Lewin, E.H.
40th Punjabis

Lewis, G.A.
Royal Engineers

Lewis, H.F.
HMS Cressy

Lidden, J.W.
Australian Imperial Force

Liddiard, T.E.
HMS Formidable

Lind, A.J.
Tank Corps

Lineham, C.
Irish Guards

Lines, G.

Lines, T.

Lingham, W.
Royal West Surrey Regiment

Lintern, J.H.A.
Royal Field Artillery

Lintott, W.J.
Royal West Surrey Regiment

Little, A.
*Duke of Cornwall's Light
Infantry*

Little, R.
1st London

Livermore, T.
6th South Wales Borderers

Lloyd, A.V.
Royal West Kent Regiment

Lock, C.

Lock, C.M.
20th Hussars

Lockewood, F.E.
Rifle Brigade

Lockewood, T.

Lodder, C.J.
2nd East Lancashire

Lomas, A.H.
2nd Devonshire

Long, L.P.
20th London

Long, W.H.
Dorsetshire Regiment

Longstaff, P.E.
Civil Service Rifles

Looseley, W.J.
Rifle Brigade

Lorenzie, D.
Cheshire Regiment

Lountain, A.M.

Love, S.C.
Royal Field Artillery

Love, W.G.
Machine Gun Corps

Lovesay, L.A.J.
3rd London

Lucas, R.
Royal West Kent Regiment

Luckett, L.P.
Rifle Brigade

Lupson, G.L.
Australian Royal Army Medical Corps

Lupton, B.

M

Macbeth, L.
HMS Astraea

Mace, E.S.
20th London

Mace, E.T.
20th London

Mace, J.
Royal Army Service Corps

Mace, J.M.
Royal Engineers

Mackenzie, J.A.

Maddox, J.W.

Maguin, F.

Maguire, T.
Royal Field Artillery

Maher, J.E.
Royal West Surrey Regiment

Mahoney, A.J.
Royal Field Artillery

Maijie, A.W.
Middlesex Regiment

Mann, F.H.
Royal Engineers

Manners, W.E.
Royal Engineers

Manning, W.
Australian Expeditionary Force

Manser, F.H.
20th London

Mansfield, J.R.
Royal Garrison Artillery

Manton, F.J.

Maples, J.W.
Royal Air Force

March, E.
East Surrey Regiment

Marcham, G.F.

Margetson, D.A.
Royal Garrison Artillery

Markin, F.E.
2nd London

Markwick, A.V.
Grenadier Guards

Marsh, H.
Royal Engineers

Marshall, C.
Royal Field Artillery

Marshall, F.G.
Royal West Kent Regiment

Marshall, T.J.
Dragoon Guards

Martin, A.
Machine Gun Corps

Martin, C.P.

Martin, H.

Martin, H.W.
2nd Royal West Kent

Martin, J.
HMS Hawke

Martin, J.
HMS Bulwark

Mason, J.W.
19th London

Mason, J.W.
Royal Field Artillery

Masters, F.W.

Matthews, A.A.
East Surrey Regiment

Mawsen, F.W.

Maxwell, R.
Royal Scots

Maynard, A.
Rifle Brigade

Maynard, A.C.
HMS Natal

McAlister, A.
Canadian Expeditionary Force

McCallum, D.D.
HMS Acteon

McClure, A.R.C.

McClure, F.R.C.

McDonald, A.
Royal Navy

McDonald, H.
Royal Field Artillery

McEwan, J.
Gordon Highlanders

McGrath, J.P.
Royal West Kent Regiment

McGregor, R.H.
Royal West Kent Regiment

McKierman, F.

McKierman, J.

McKnight, W.
8th London

McNab, R.
16th Lancers

McNab, W.J.
ss Keeling

Meakins, C.
1st Bedfordshire

Medhurst, W.R.
HMS Cressy

Mee, A.

Mee, P.W.
29th Canadian Light Horse

Mees, H.
Royal West Kent Regiment

Melbourne, E.H.
Royal West Kent Regiment

Melbourne, F.
3rd Hussars

Melhuish, C.
Royal Army Service Corps Motor Transport

Meloy, A.
Royal Field Artillery

Meloy, A.E.
Royal Field Artillery

Meloy, J.J.
20th London

Merrett, F.
Royal Army Ordnance Corps

Merrett, H.
Royal West Kent Regiment

Merrett, W.

Merritt, A.
20th London

Merritt, E.G.
3rd Fusiliers

Merritt, H.W.
Royal West Kent Regiment

Merritt, J.W.
HMS Natal

Merritt, W.
20th London

Merton, W.
Rifle Brigade

Meyer, L.G.
20th London

Middleton, D.J.
Royal West Kent Regiment

Miller, F.H.
Royal Berkshire

Miller, G.
Royal West Kent Regiment

Miller, J.H.
Royal Berkshire Regiment

Miller, W.C.
20th London

Mills, A.J.
Royal Engineers

Milsom, G.W.

Milton, F.W.
20th London

Minchin, J.

Minter, A.E.
HMS Galatea

Mires, B.

Mitchel, H.

Mitchel, T.S.
King's Royal Rifle Corps

Mitchell, A.G.
Lincolnshire Regiment

Mitchenson, J.S.
Royal Horse Artillery

Molley, E.
20th London

Molton, A.T.
Gordon Highlanders

Moltt, W.H.
Royal Field Artillery

Monk, W.W.
Royal Garrison Artillery

Moody, A.J.

Moody, J.

Moody, S.A.
Royal Field Artillery

Moon, F.W.
20th London

Moore, C.
Labour Corps

Moore, E.C.

Moore, H.F.P.

Moorehouse, C.G.

Moores, P.
8th London

Moreland, A.
Tank Corps

Moreland, W.
Royal Garrison Artillery

Morgan, C.V.
Rifle Brigade

Morgan, T.A.
HMS Hogue

Morgan, W.H.
6th Hampshire

Morphew, G.A.
HMS Hampshire

Morris, J.

Morris, J.W.
Royal West Kent Regiment

Morris, T.

Morris, V.J.
King's Royal Rifle Corps

Morrison, H.F.
Royal West Kent Regiment

Morsley, F.G.

Mortimer, H.S.

Moutrie, B.

Moyce, J.
Royal West Kent Regiment

Mudge, B.H.

Mudge, E.J.

Mulcock, A.

Munday, A.H.

Munday, W.J.
Royal Engineers

Mundell, F.

Murphy, J.

Murrell, W.H.
23rd London

Murton, W.T.
Rifle Brigade

N

Neal, J.F.
Royal Marine Light Infantry

Neal, J.R.

Neale, R.J.
Royal West Surrey Regiment

Neck, F.C.
5th London

Neeman, J.J.
Royal West Kent Regiment

Neighbour, J.

Netley, A.J.

Netley, G.R.
4th Middlesex

Neville, G.
Royal Army Service Corps

Neville, W.
Royal Engineers

New, F.

New, J.
HMS Hogue

Newhold, W.T.
1st Borderers

Newman, G.A.

Newman, G.A.W.
20th London

Newman, W.H.

Newman, W.J.

Newstead, A.J.
20th London

Nichol, J.O.L.
58th Vaughan's Rifles, Frontier Force Indian

Nicholls, J.W.
Royal Fusiliers

Nicholson, C.H.
Royal Engineers

Nicholson, H.W.
Cheshire Regiment

Nicholson, T.R.

Nick, A.E.
Rifle Brigade

Nick, A.J.

Nightingale, G.W.

Nightingale, H.B.
Royal Garrison Artillery

Nightingale, L.E.

Nixon, J.W.
Royal Air Force

Noakes, C.
Rifle Brigade

Noakes, S.
20th London

Noakes, W.T.
3rd Worcestershire

Nobbs, N.

Nock, E.
Rifle Brigade

Nock, R.
Royal Field Artillery

Norfolk, H.
13th Hussars

Norman, A.E.
Royal Horse Artillery

Norman, E.C.

Norrie, A.
9th Norfolk

Norris, G.

Norris, H.A.R.

Norris, S.F.

North, G.

Northcott, A.
HMS Cressy

Nott, E.
Rifle Brigade

O

O'Conner, T.
Royal Naval Air Service

O'Connor, E.

O'Leary, M.J.
East Surrey Regiment

O'Rourke, M.
Argyll & Sutherland Highlanders

O'Sullivan, P.
Labour Corps

Oak, H.G.
Royal Field Artillery

Oak, J.H.

Oakes, A.V.
Royal West Kent Regiment

Oakley, B.T.
19th London

Ogden, W.J.
Royal West Kent Regiment

Old, F.H.
London Regiment

Oldridge, H.C.
Royal Army Service Corps

Oliver, J.H.
Royal Army Ordnance Corps

Oliver, S.
Royal Garrison Artillery

Omans, E.

Ommanney, A.H.

Ommanney, R.
Royal Engineers

Oswald, W.D.
West Yorkshire Regiment
DISTINGUISHED SERVICE ORDER

Otten, E.J.
Rifle Brigade

Ottley, H.G.
Connaught Rangers

Ottley, T.W.
*Royal Army Ordnance
Department*

Owen, H.C.
HMS Minotaur

Owen, J.
20th London

Owens, J.
Labour Corps

P

Packer, F.

Packer, J.W.

Packer, W.C.
Royal Irish Rifles

Packman, B.
Royal West Kent Regiment

Padfield, C.J.C.
Middlesex Regiment

Page, E.B.
HMS Defence

Pain, W.
Royal Field Artillery

Palmer, A.

Palmer, E.
HMS Vanguard

Panter, H.C.
Royal Field Artillery

Park, E.G.T.
25th London

Parke, F.T.
Royal Navy

Parker, C.
East Surrey Regiment

Parker, E.E.
21st London

Parker, H.A.
HMS Warrior

Parker, H.C.
6th City of London

Parkinson, E.G.
53rd Australian Imperial Force

Parkinson, G.M.
35th Australian Imperial Force

Parks, F.W.
45th Training Reserve Battalion

Parr, A.
HMS Hawke

Parrott, G.F.
East Kent Regiment

Parrott, T.
HMS Lord Nelson

Patrick, H.J.
3rd London

Patrick, S.A.
17th London

Patterson, H.F.
HMS Pembroke

Pay, L.

Payne, A.G.
20th London

Payne, H.G.
Honourable Artillery Company

Payne, H.G.
East Kent Regiment

Paynter, T.P.
Royal Sussex Regiment

Peach, J.H.
Northumberland Fusiliers

Peacocks, A.J.
Middlesex Regiment

Peacocks, J.C.
East Surrey Regiment

Peake, W.H.

Pearce, A.E.

Pearce, C.
Canadian Expeditionary Force

Pearce, T.
East Kent Regiment

Pease, E.J.
10th Royal Sussex

Pedder, C.
HMS Invincible

Peddlesden, W.H.

Pell, H.

Pellerow, F.S.
Rifle Brigade

Pellett, G.A.V.
HMS Hogue

Penfield, H.J.

Penfold, B.H.

Percival, A.
Royal Engineers

Perkins, O.R.
HMS Formidable

Perrott, P.

Perry, A.S.
20th London

Perry, C.C.

Peskett, G.R.
Royal West Kent Regiment

Peskett, M.
King's Royal Rifle Corps

Peskett, T.
Royal West Kent Regiment

Peters, J.
Royal West Kent Regiment

Peters, W.H.
2nd Suffolk

Phillips, A.F.
Essex Regiment

Phillips, G.A.
Royal Field Artillery

Phillips, R.
Royal Army Service Corps

Phillips, W.A.
Royal Garrison Artillery

Pick, G.F.
2nd Border

Pickersgill, J.H.
Rifle Brigade

Pierce, C.

Pilbrow, S.

Pinder, P.
Rifle Brigade

Pink, H.J.

Pinson, R.E.S.
Royal West Kent Regiment

Pitman, A.G.
Machine Gun Corps

Pitts, H.E.
Royal Field Artillery

Plowman, F.
Scottish Rifles

Plowman, H.
Scottish Rifles

Plowman, H.L.
Canadian Scottish Rifles

Plum, W.
Royal Horse Artillery

Pollard, F.
20th London

Pollard, F.T.
20th London

Pollard, W.A.
20th London

Pollard, W.H.
7th Canadian

Pollard, W.S.

Pope, E.N.

Pope, W.S.
20th London

Porter, G.
Royal West Surrey Regiment

Potter, G.J.N.

Potts, C.L.
1st North Staffordshire

Potts, L.V.

Powell, E.N.
Royal West Kent Regiment

Powell, G.
Royal Army Service Corps

Powell, N.L.
Royal Field Artillery

Prangley, W.H.
Royal Garrison Artillery

Pratt, C.
London Regiment

Prentiss, S.B.
HMS Pathfinder

Press, H.E.
15th London

Price, F.

Price, F.C.

Price, J.
Rifle Brigade

Price, J.B.

Price, J.W.

Price, M.B.
Royal Warwickshire Regiment

Price, R.A.
19th London

Price, W.
Machine Gun Corps

Priddis, W.G.J.
20th London

Prosser, J.B.
20th London

Puckett, F.
East Kent Regiment

Puplett, W.F.
Royal West Kent Regiment

Purser, J.
20th London

Purvis, L.
London Scottish

Puttock, S.

R

Radford, F.S.
London Rifle Brigade

Ramster, W.W.

Rance, A.
4th Training Reserve Battalion

Ransley, R.
Labour Corps

Ranson, S.G.
Royal Engineers

Ratton, W.H.
22nd London

Rawlings, J.E.
HMS Hogue

Rawlings, W.B.
HMS Natal

Rawson, S.M.
20th Royal Fusiliers

Rawston, F.B.
6th City of London

Rawston, W.W.
5th Middlesex

Raymond, G.

Read, S.

Realff, G.W.

Reaney, M.F.

Redmond, F.

Reece, C.
East Surrey Regiment

Reed, C.H.
King's Shropshire Light Infantry

Reed, J.T.

Reed, W.G.
Labour Corps

Rees, A.C.
East Surrey Regiment

Reeves, C.H.
Machine Gun Corps

Reiss, S.L.

Revell, S.H.
HMS Mentor

Reynolds, J.T.

Rhodes, H.

Ribbins, W.M.
West Yorkshire Regiment

Richards, A.E.

Richards, T.A.
Royal Engineers

Richards, W.
Royal Field Artillery

Richardson, H.A.

Richer, A.S.

Richmond, H.S.
1st Honourable Artillery
Company

Rickett, R.R.
HMS Dreel Castle

Rickett, S.
Royal Field Artillery

Rickman, A.J.

Rickman, W.

Rington, A.
Middlesex Regiment

Rink, H.J.

Rixon, F.

Roberts, A.
Royal West Kent Regiment

Roberts, F.
Royal West Kent Regiment

Roberts, J.W.
Cameron Highlanders

Roberts,
Royal West Surrey Regiment

Robertson, J.

Robins, J.A.
HMS Bacchante

Robins, W.J.
Machine Gun Corps

Robinson, A.
Royal Inniskilling Fusiliers

Robinson, P.
5th Rifle Brigade

Rofe, C.
Somerset Light Infantry

Rogers, A.F.
Royal Air Force

Rogers, B.
Royal West Kent Regiment

Rogers, F.
Royal Air Force

Rogers, J.B.
Royal Welsh Fusiliers

Rogers, W.
17th London

Rogers, W.J.
Rifle Brigade

Rollins, W.

Roman, R.M.

Rose, A.A.
ss Telconia

Rose, G.W.

Rose, H.
8th East Surrey

Ross, J.
HMS Carnation

Ross, J.
King's Royal Rifle Corps

Rowan, R.M.J.
City of London

Rowsell, W.C.
HMS Defence

Rowton, W.W.
3rd Middlesex

Royston, J.
Royal Air Force

Rudd, A.G.

Rumney, J.
1st East Kent

Rumsey, A.T.
Royal Field Artillery

Rumsey, D.

Rush, B.W.
Royal Horse Artillery

Russell, A.
Royal Field Artillery

Russell, A.E.
Royal Fusiliers

Russell, A.G.
East Kent Regiment

Russell, E.J.
Royal Army Medical Corps

Russell, J.
Royal Fusiliers

Russell, S.
King's Royal Rifle Corps

Russell, W.
HMS Defence

Russell, W.G.
17th London

Rutter, F.N.
Royal Fusiliers

Ryan, J.
20th London

S

Sack, H.L.

Salmon, A.
Middlesex Regiment

Salter-Gibson, A.

Sampson, F.

Samson, G.D.
Royal Navy

Samson, H.E.

Sanders, F.

Sanders, P.T.

Sanders, S.W.
Royal Field Artillery

Sands, P.

Santer, A.C.

Santer, J.
Royal West Kent Regiment

Sarage, A.

Saunders, A.W.
West Yorkshire Regiment

Saunders, E.B.

Saunders, J.J.
20th London

Saunders, L.

Saunderson, W.J.
HMS Hannibal

Savage, J.L.

Saveall, W.J.
Rifle Brigade

Savill, J.E.
Rifle Brigade

Saw, A.C.
Royal Naval Air Service

Saw, N.H.W.
Royal Army Medical Corps

Saywer, A.J.

Scholey, P.W.

Scoging, C.E.

Scoging, H.

Scoltcock, H.R.

Scotney, A.G.

Scrutton, H.U.
1st Northumberland Fusiliers

Sculley, J.

Seagrove, E.
Duke of Cornwall's Light Infantry

Seagrove, T.
Dragoon Guards

Seal, W.
Northumberland Fusiliers

Searl, H.
HMS Bacchus

Searle, J.
Royal Air Force

Searle, W.

Searles, W.A.
Royal Field Artillery

Sears, G.E.
19th London

Seaton, C.G.
14th London Scottish

Self, F.
Brigade of Guards

Selfe, W.M.
4th London

Sellers, W.

Sewell, A.W.
Rifle Brigade

Sewell, C.H.
Tank Corps
VICTORIA CROSS

Sewell, H.K.
Royal Field Artillery

Sewell, H.V.
Royal Field Artillery

Sexton, A.

Seymour, H.S.
Rifle Brigade

Shelbrook, H.E.
Rifle Brigade

Shelton, F.
Royal West Kent Regiment

Shepard, C.H.
Devonshire Regiment

Sheppard, C.A.
HMS Aboukir

Sheppard, W.
Royal Field Artillery

Shepperd, J.
20th London

Sheppey, J.R.

Sherbourne, W.
London Regiment

Sherman, H.F.
Royal Horse Artillery

Sherman, R.
Royal Army Medical Corps

Shorter, R.
HMS Vanguard

Shrewsbury, J.

Shurly, L.
20th London

Silcox, E.
HMS Vanguard

Simmonds, T.P.
Nottinghamshire & Derby

Simmons, G.F.
HMS Black Prince

Simmons, J.P.
Sherwood Foresters

Simms, C.

Simms, W.
Royal Warwickshire Regiment

Simpson, A.
Royal Garrison Artillery

Simpson, H.
Duke of Cornwall's Light Infantry

Sims, C.R.
Royal Field Artillery

Sinclair, C.S.

Sinfield, A.E.
HM Submarine K17

Sinkin, J.H.
Royal Army Service Corps

Sissons, J.
King's Royal Rifle Corps

Skelton, C.
Royal West Kent Regiment

Sketchley, G.H.A.
City of London

Skinner, W.
Rifle Brigade

Skinner, W.E.
Royal Flying Corps

Slack, F.
Royal West Kent Regiment

Slator, G.
Royal Naval Division

Slator, G.B.
Rifle Brigade

Smart, C.
Rifle Brigade

Smith, A.C.
Royal Engineers

Smith, A.J.
20th London

Smith, A.W.
1st African Rifles

Smith, A.W.
Naval Reserve

Smith, C.H.
London Regiment

Smith, C.H.
London Regiment

Smith, E.H.
Royal Army Vetinary Corps

Smith, F.
Royal West Kent Regiment

Smith, F.
Duke of Cornwall's Light Infantry

Smith, F.
HMS Hawke

Smith, F.J.
Royal West Kent Regiment

Smith, G.F.
HMS Lancaster

Smith, H.
20th London

Smith, H.G.

Smith, H.L.
King's Liverpool Regiment

Smith, J.
Dorsetshire Regiment

Smith, J.C.
20th London

Smith, J.E.G.
Royal Horse Artillery

Smith, J.G.
HMS Bulwark

Smith, M.
Rifle Brigade

Smith, O.
King's Royal Rifle Corps

Smith, R.
Royal Fusiliers

Smith, R.A.

Smith, R.A.S.
Royal Field Artillery

Smith, S.
London Regiment

Smith, S.G.W.
20th London

Smith, S.H.
1st London

Smith, T.S.
20th London

Smith, W.E.
Royal Garrison Artillery

Smith, W.T.
Civil Service Rifles

Smoker, A.H.
Rifle Brigade

Smyth, J.
Rifle Brigade

Snell, E.E.
Northumberland Fusiliers

Somerwell, E.H.
11th Essex

Sorrell, E.A.
17th Yorkshire

Spanton, A.P.
Honourable Artillery Company

Spark, J.
East Yorkshire

Sparkey, A.

Sparks, A.
Rifle Brigade

Spencer, A.E.
11th Hussars

Spencer, A.H.
HMS Blonde

Spencer, H.
East Kent Regiment

Spencerey, A.T.
Royal Army Service Corps

Spicer, C.J.
King's Royal Rifle Corps

Spooner, A.T.

Springett, A.
Royal West Kent Regiment

Staines, J.W.
Royal Irish Fusiliers

Stanbridge, J.
Royal Fusiliers

Staneley, J.

Stanford, J.F.
Devonshire Regiment

Stanley, G.W.

Stanley, T.J.
5th Middlesex

Stanley, W.J.
7th Kings Royal Rifles

Stanley, W.J.J.
Yacht Patrol

Stannard, G.

Stannard, G.W.
Royal Garrison Artillery

Staples, H.

Stapleton, T.
Royal West Kent Regiment

Stapley, A.J.F.
Rifle Brigade

Starkey, A.
Royal West Kent Regiment

Staton, A.
Royal Fusiliers

Staveley, J.W.
Leicestershire

Steggles, T.W.
HMS Indefatigable

Stephens, C.H.
King's Royal Rifle Corps

Stephens, T.R.

Stephenson, A.E.

Stevens, A.N.
20th London

Stevens, D.B.
Duke of Cornwall's Light Infantry

Stevens, T.
7th Middlesex

Stevens, W.J.
18th London

Stevenson, F.J.
Royal West Kent Regiment

Stewart, E.T.
London Regiment

Stewart, W.
Suffolk Regiment

Stokes, J.

Stokesbury, F.H.
Royal Garrison Artillery

Stone, A.
Lancashire Fusiliers
DISTINGUISHED
SERVICE ORDER

Stone, H.
King's Royal Rifle Corps

Stone, H.P.

Stone, P.E.
Rifle Brigade

Stone, R.
Royal Air Force

Stone, W.N.
Royal Fusiliers
VICTORIA CROSS

Stopford, H.

Storrs, H.L.
Royal Air Force

Street, L.
Royal West Kent Regiment

Stringman, G.J.
Royal West Surrey Regiment

Stroud, J.S.
HMS Dragon

Strudwick, G.

Strutt, H.F.
Royal Garrison Artillery

Sturgess, C.
HMS Hebe

Sturgess, S.
Royal West Sussex

Sturgiss, H.W.
102nd Training Reserve Battalion

Sturgiss, J.
19th London

Sullivan, D.
Royal West Kent Regiment

Sullivan, T.
Rifle Brigade

Swain, F.G.
Royal West Kent Regiment

Swallow, W.H.
Royal Army Ordnance Corps

Swandale, H.W.
14th Company Labour Corps

Swayne, S.C.
East Kent Regiment

Swift, C.W.
East Surrey Regiment

Swift, W.J.
Hampshire Regiment

T

Taber, J.E.
Royal West Kent Regiment

Taken, W.J.
HM Destroyer No. 10

Tandy, F.W.
2nd Dragoon Guards

Taylor, F.J.
Rifle Brigade

Taylor, H.C.

Taylor, J.
Middlesex Regiment

Taylor, T.H.
East Yorkshire Regiment

Taylor, W.H.

Taylor, W.I.
North Lancashire Regiment

Taylor, W.W.
Royal West Kent Regiment

Temple, F.
Royal Army Service Corps

Temple, F.S.
Middlesex Regiment

Temple, F.T.

Terry, F.C.

Terry, F.G.
East Kent Regiment

Terry, F.T.
Royal Horse Guards

Terry, W.E. (Jnr)
Royal Army Medical Corps

Terry, W.E. (Snr)

Terry, W.J.
1st Suffolks

Thomas, H.
HMS Vanguard

Thomas, J.E.

Thomas, S.H.

Thomas, T.J.
Royal Fusiliers

Thomas, T.W.
Royal Field Artillery

Thompson, E.F.
Royal Engineers

Thompson, F.G.
Royal Field Artillery

Thompson, H.
Royal Air Force

Thompson, R.C.
Royal Berkshire

Thompson, S.F.H.
Royal Air Force

Thompson, T.J.
Royal Fusiliers

Thomson, H.G.
Rifle Brigade

Thorndyke, C.J.
Hampshire Regiment

Thornhill, W.
4th Hussars

Thornton, A.G.
HMT Pathon

Thornton, C.A.

Thornton, C.W.
Machine Gun Corps

Thornton, H.
Royal Lancashire Fusiliers

Thornton, H.C.
*Oxfordshire & Buckinghamshire
Light Infantry*

Thorogood, H.
15th London

Thorogood, J.C.
4th Training Reserve Battalion

Thorpe, C.
5th London

Thorsby, A.
21st London

Thrasher, C.J.
13th Rifle Brigade

Tibbles, J.A.
East Kent Regiment

Tibbles, J.M.
HMS Invincible

Tickner, A.

Tobin, J.
Royal West Kent Regiment

Toffs, H.

Tolhurst, G.
East Kent Regiment

Tombs, H.
Honourable Artillery Company

Tombs, J.
Royal Fusiliers

Tomlinson, G.F.
King's Royal Rifle Corps

Tookey, J.W.
Labour Corps

Tovell, W. Jnr

Tovell, W. Snr
Royal West Kent Regiment

Townsend, F.B.

Tremearne, A.J.N.
Seaforth Highlanders

Tremearne, W.C.
Seaforth Highlanders

Tritschler, H.J.
Devonshire Regiment

Truett, E.C.

Tucker, J.

Tuffs, W.C.
Royal Canadian Regiment

Tullett, W.H.
Royal West Kent Regiment

Tumber, E.D.
Royal West Kent Regiment

Tumber, G.E.
19th London

Tumber, J.
Rifle Brigade

Tumber, J.R.
HMS Vanguard

Turley, W.
Middlesex Regiment

Turner, A.R.
20th London

Turner, G.
Rifle Brigade

Turner, G.J.

Turner, W.G.
Royal Field Artillery

Turner, W.S.

Tutt, E.
Royal Navy

Twelvetree, C.
Machine Gun Corps

Twin, F.C.

Twinn, C.F.
East Kent Regiment

Tyler, F.
Royal Marine Light Infantry

U

Ulvemacher, E.V.
1st Essex

Underwood, J.
Royal Field Artillery

V

Vane, T.G.
20th London

Varndell, S.H.
14th Essex

Vigar, E.
Royal Yorkshire

Vince, A.
HMS Clarion

Vincent, J.G.
Royal Engineers

Vincent, J.J.
Royal West Surrey Regiment

Vincent, J.R.
Royal Sussex Regiment

Vrotte, A.
Middlesex Regiment

Vyar, E.

W

Wade, A.A.
3rd Hussars

Waghorn, E.
1st Middlesex

Waghorn, J.F.
King's Royal Rifle Corps

Waghorn, L.P.
Royal West Kent Regiment

Waghorn, W.
Royal West Kent Regiment

Waite, C.W.
HMS Hawke

Walder, A.S.C.
London Regiment

Waldie, J.A.
HMS Inflexible

Walker, C.W.
Grenadier Guards

Walker, G.R.
King's Royal Rifle Corps

Walker, J.H.A.
Royal Surrey

Walker, R.
20th London

Walker, S.R.
Somerset Light Infantry

Walker, W.G.

Walker, W.R.
Labour Corps

Wall, J.
Labour Corps

Waller, H.G.
Royal West Kent Regiment

Walter, J.F.

Walter, W.G.
1st Lincolnshire

Walter, W.J.
Royal Marine Light Infantry

Want, L.P.

Waples, J.W.

Ward, C.W.A.

Ward, H.A.W.
Grenadier Guards

Ward, J.B.
16th Northumberland Fusiliers

Ward, S.F.

Ward, T.
3rd London

Warman, A.E.

Warren, E.D.
Middlesex Regiment

Watkinson, A.E.
Royal Army Medical Corps

Watkinson, A.F.
Royal Air Force

Watkinson, S.

Watling, A.
3rd Rifle Brigade

Watling, S.

Watson, F.
East Kent Regiment

Watson, J.R.
12th Rifle Brigade

Watson, S.
HMS Indomitable

Watt, E.L.
Royal Field Artillery

Watt, F.E.
HMS Salta

Waugh, E.G.
14th South Lancashire

Waugh, G.
6th South Lancashire

Webb, F.C.
Rifle Brigade

Webb, J.D.

Webb, M.

Webber, W.F.
HMS Black Prince

Webber, W.F.
7th Middlesex

Webster, B.F.
7th Middlesex

Webster, W.L.
7th Middlesex

Weeden, F.

Welkins, J.

Wellard, A.F.

Wells, G.W.

Wells, J.T.
Royal Army Service Corps

Welsh, F.W.
King's Royal Rifle Corps

Welsh, W.C.
Royal Engineers

Wenham, G.
Rifle Brigade

West, A.

Weston, W.
HMS Kale

Weymouth, A.E.
Royal Army Service Corps

Wharam, R.W.

Wharf, G.J.

Wheate, A.
28th London

White, A.G.
Coldstream Guards

White, A.G.
Royal West Kent Regiment

White, A.J.
King's Royal Rifle Corps

White, A.W.

White, F.
Royal West Kent Regiment

White, F.E.
Royal West Kent Regiment

White, G.G.
2nd London

White, G.J.
East Kent Regiment

White, H.T.

White, I.G.

White, J.
Northamptonshire Regiment

White, J.S.V.
Royal Field Artillery

White, L.S.
Royal West Kent Regiment

White, W.H.
9th Worcesters

White, W.T.
City of London

Whitehouse, R.A.
Gloucestershire Regiment

Whitlock, B.S.
7th London

Widgery, P.H.

Wiggins, A.J.
Royal Field Artillery

Wilcox, G.
Royal West Kent Regiment

Wild, F.
Somerset Light Infantry

Wild, G.
Northumberland Fusiliers

Wilicox, C.

Wilkins, J.
King's Royal Rifle Corps

Wilkinson, S.
Royal Garrison Artillery

Willeston, R.
Wiltshire Regiment

Williams, E.

Williams, E.D.

Williams, F.

Williams, J.H.
Royal Field Artillery

Williams, J.J.
Rifle Brigade

Williams, M.

Williams, W.R.
Royal Field Artillery

Willis, A.
Royal Engineers

Willis, E.C.
Royal West Kent Regiment

Willmott, A.L.
Royal Army Vetinary Corps

Willsher, L.A.
Lancashire Fusiliers

Willsher, W.A.
23rd Royal Fusiliers

Wilson, R.G.

Wilston, R.W.

Winch, E.H.
Highland Light Infantry

Winder, H.C.
3rd London

Windsor, A.P.

Windsor, H.W.

Winter, A.G.
London Regiment

Winterburn, H.A.
Royal Field Artillery

Wiseman, W.F.

Wolfe, D.R.
Royal Berkshire Regiment

Wolfe, R.

Wood, H.J.
East Kent Regiment

Wood, W.F.

Wooderson, J.R.
20th London

Woodford, H.

Woodford, R.

Woodgate, C.
Royal West Kent Regiment

Woodhouse, R.

Woodmore, T.H.
Welsh Guards

Woodrow, W.H.
Royal Field Artillery

Wookey, G.R.P.
3rd East Yorkshire

Woolard, G.

Woolard, H.G.
20th London

Woolford, H.

Woolford, R.
Royal West Kent Regiment

Woolley, H.G.
8th Royal West Kent

Worsell, A.
Royal Army Vetinary Corps

Worthy, E.H.
1st London

Wortley, R.
Royal Fusiliers

Wortten, P.
East Surrey Regiment

Wray, J.W.
Northumberland Fusiliers

Wright, C.
Royal Field Artillery

Wright, E.A.
20th London

Wright, G.A.P.
Machine Gun Corps

Wright, G.T.
East Kent Regiment

Wright, H.O.
Royal Fusiliers

Wright, L.C.
Royal West Surrey Regiment

Wright, W.J.
Royal Garrison Artillery

Wykes, A.
Royal West Kent Regiment

Wynn, J.
Royal Field Artillery

Y

York, C.H.
20th London

York, H.
20th London

Young, A.E.
20th London

Young, J.D.
1st/6th KRR

Young, L.A.

Young, W.T.T.
Officers' Training Corps

Z

Zeitz, A.

Local Memorials in Pictures

The Grade II listed memorial is made from Portland stone. It's about 12 feet tall and was designed in a classical style with a moulded cornice and three panels divided by Ionic pilasters.

Remembrance service in progress. (Photo: Brian Aldrich)

The central panel of the War Memorial bears the coat of arms for the Metropolitan Borough of Greenwich. The borough motto was Tempore Utimur ("We make use of time").

TO THE GLORY OF GOD ❦ IN MEMORY OF PARISHIONERS AND MEMBERS OF THE CONGREGATION OF S.ᵗ ALFEGE GREENWICH WHO DIED FOR THEIR COUNTRY IN THE GREAT WAR 1914-1918 OR IN THE EXPEDITIONS OF 1919 AND 1920

ALFRED ADAMS
FREDERICK J. ALDRICK
ALBERT ANDERSON
HENRY ANDERSON
JOHN BARKER
FREDERICK E. BATEMAN
JOSEPH H. BATEMAN
GEORGE BAULSON
HENRY BAULSON
JOHN T. BAULSON
RICHARD BAULSON
JOHN BETTS
JAMES R. BLOOMFIELD
FRANK E. BRANT
JAMES W. BREACKER
ALFRED J. BROWN
CHARLES J. BRUNNING
JOHN H. BUCKELL
GEORGE H. BULLOCK
HERBERT C. BULLOCK
FRANK D. BURGESS
CHARLES BUSSEY
ARTHUR W. CHISMON
HENRY G. CLARK
EDWARD R. COOK
CECIL W. COONEY
JOHN CRAZE
ERNEST C. CROUCH
RICHARD E. DABIN
WILLIAM E. DANIELS
CHARLES W. DAW
THOMAS DAWES
WALTER I. DELL
HENRY H. DILKS M.M
GEORGE F. DILLON
CONRAD H. DINWIDDY
ARTHUR O. DRIVER
GEORGE EDWARDS

FREDERICK C. EDWARDS
WILLIAM C. ELGAR
HAROLD G. EVERSON
JOHN A. FIELD
SIDNEY FINCH
THOMAS W. FLANDERS
JOSEPH FLINT
HENRY FOX
ALFRED FREEMAN
DAVID J. FREEMAN
HERBERT J. FRIDAY
WILLIAM G. FRIDAY
JOHN GALLAGHER
ALBERT A. GAMBLING
LESLIE T. GARRETT
HARRY R. GATES
ARTHUR H. GIBBS
JOHN J. GILROY
WILLIAM A. GOBLE
CLAUDE V. GOLLE
WILLIAM GREENHILL
ALEXANDER GREIG
WILLIAM A. GROOMBRIDGE
ROBERT H. GROVES V.C.
COLIN G. HALL
HORACE F. HARDY
FREDERICK HATTEMORE
GEORGE H. HAYWARD
GEORGE W. HEASMAN
FRANCIS J. HENNESSEY
ALFRED J. HIGGINS
HARRY C. HILL
CHARLES W. HOBBS
ERNEST A. HOBBS D.C.M
JAMES HOWES
ERIC B. HURST
ALFRED S. HUMPHRYS
ARTHUR G. JACKSON

ARTHUR W. JACOBS
ROBERT J. JAMES
HARRY JELF
WALTER JENKINS
ALBERT M. JESSUP
HENRY G. JONES
JAMES H. JONES
WILLIAM KANE
ROY C. KEEBLE
ARCHIBALD G. KEEL
HORATIO H. KILBY
ARTHUR KINGTON
FRANK D. KYLE
THOMAS KYLE
JOHN B. LANGLER M.C
EDWARD T. LARKING
HENRY G. LAWRENCE
ARTHUR J. LILLEY
ROBERT D. LITTLE
FREDERICK H. MANSER M.M.
ARCHIE L. MANSER
FREDERICK J. MANTON
JOSEPH MARTER
HORACE McDONALD
FRANK MELBOURNE
GEORGE W. MILLER
BERNARD MIRES
CYRIL V. MORGAN
THOMAS MORRIS
ALBERT H. MUNDAY
JOHN T. NEIGHBOUR
CECIL NOAKES
STANLEY NOAKES
NELSON NOBBS
MICHAEL J. O'LEARY
HENRY G. OTTLEY
EDWARD PARKER
HAROLD A. PARKER
THOMAS A. PARROTT
BERNARD H. PENFOLD
ALFRED S. PERRY
TIMOTHY C. PESKETT
MICHAEL PESKETT
GEORGE P. PESKETT
PERCY PINDER
MARSHALL B. PRICE

LIONEL PURVIS
WALTER G. REED
WILLIAM M. J. RIBBINS
FREDERICK W. RIXON
ALEXIS E. ROBINSON
JOHN B. ROGERS
FREDERICK N. RUTTER
PERCIVAL SANDS
PERCY W. SCHOLEY
WILLIAM SEARLE
HENRY SEARLE
CECIL H. SEWELL V.C.
HARRY K. SEWELL
HERBERT V. SEWELL
EDWARD W. SEWELL
REGINALD SHERMAN
HUBERT D. SMITH
JAMES C. SMITH
OWEN SMITH
ROY SMITH
JACK SMYTH
ERNEST E. SNELL
ERNEST H. SOMERWELL
ALBERT E. SPENCER
ALFRED H. SPENCER
CHARLES H. STEPHENS
HENRY P. STONE
CHARLES STURGESS
SAMUEL STURGESS
HEDLEY F. STRUTT
FRANK S. TEMPLE
GEORGE T. TURNER
WILLIAM G. TURNER
ERNEST WAGHORN
WILLIAM WAGHORN
THOMAS WARD
ALFRED E. WARMAN
WILLIAM WESTON
THOMAS G. WHITE
ALFRED J. WIGGINS
FREDERICK WILD
GEORGE WILD
EDWARD C. WILLIS
HARRY K. WOOLLARD
JAMES D. YOUNG

St Alfege Church has two boards listing parishioners killed during WWI.

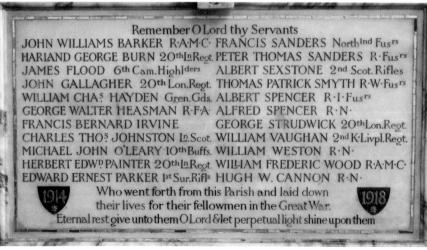

Remember O Lord thy Servants

JOHN WILLIAMS BARKER R·A·M·C· FRANCIS SANDERS North¹ⁿᵈ Fusʳˢ
HARLAND GEORGE BURN 20ᵗʰLⁿ.Reɡt. PETER THOMAS SANDERS R·Fusʳˢ
JAMES FLOOD 6ᵗʰ Cam.Highlᵈᵉʳˢ ALBERT SEXSTONE 2ⁿᵈ Scot.Rifles
JOHN GALLAGHER 20ᵗʰ Lon.Reɡt. THOMAS PATRICK SMYTH R·W·Fusʳˢ
WILLIAM CHAˢ HAYDEN Grⁿ.Gds. ALBERT SPENCER R·I·Fusʳˢ
GEORGE WALTER HEASMAN R·F·A· ALFRED SPENCER R·N·
FRANCIS BERNARD IRVINE GEORGE STRUDWICK 20ᵗʰLon.Reɡt.
CHARLES THOˢ JOHNSTON Lⁿ.Scot. WILLIAM VAUGHAN 2ⁿᵈ K·Livpl.Reɡt.
MICHAEL JOHN O'LEARY 10ᵗʰBuffs. WILLIAM WESTON R·N·
HERBERT EDWᴰ PAINTER 20ᵗʰLⁿ.Reɡt. WILLIAM FREDERIC WOOD R·A·M·C·
EDWARD ERNEST PARKER 1ˢᵗ Sur.Riflˢ HUGH W. CANNON R·N·

1914   Who went forth from this Parish and laid down
their lives for their fellowmen in the Great War.   1918
Eternal rest give unto them O Lord & let perpetual light shine upon them

Memorial tablet inside Our Ladye Star of the Sea Church on Crooms Hill.

South Metropolitan Gas Workers Memorial on the Greenwich Peninsula with the gas holder in the background. It was moved here after the construction of the Millennium Dome. It has the names of 79 workers inscribed on it and was Grade II listed in October 2018.

Memorial at John Roan School.
(Photo: Lorena Woodfine).

20th London Regiment memorial on Blackheath.

Charlton Village War Memorial was erected next to St Luke's Church in 1920 - two years earlier than the Metropolitan Borough's memorial. It was Grade II listed in 2016.

War Memorial at Greenwich Cemetery with The City in the distance. The cemetery, off Well Hall Road SE9, was established in 1856 and has over 560 WWI burials according to the Commonwealth War Graves Commission.

Other memorials within the boundaries of what is now the Royal Borough of Greenwich include the Ypres Memorial Milestone on Shooters Hill, Woolwich New Cemetery War Memorial (photo: Chris Mansfield) and Eltham War Memorial (photo: Brian Aldrich).

Thank you

Thank you to these organisations and individuals for their support in publishing the Greenwich Roll of Honour: 1914-1918

The Royal Borough of Greenwich
The Greenwich Society
Greenwich Historical Society

St Alfege Church, Greenwich
The Trafalgar Tavern
Warwick Leadlay Gallery

Richard Upton
The Friends of St Alfege Church
Our Ladye Star of the Sea Church
Greenwich Industrial History Society

The Blackheath Society
Army Cadets Force, Blackheath
Sabo's Newsagent
Old Cottage Coffee Shop, Charlton

Brian Aldrich	Jim Gillman	Revd Canon Chris Moody
Richard Baglin	Cllr Matt Hartley	Mary Ney
Horatio Blood	Barbara Holland	Elizabeth Pearcey
Cllr Geoff Brighty	Cllr Denise Hyland	Neil Rhind MBE
Elizabeth Cooper	Judy Kent	Father Kevin Robinson
Anthony Cross	Peter Kent	Cllr Aidan Smith
Frank Dowling	Jonathan Louth	Cllr Danny Thorpe
Cllr John Fahy	Rachel Mawhood	Pieter van der Merwe MBE
Cllr Nigel Fletcher	Chris Mansfield	Bernadette Vizena
Janet Gillman	Mary Mills	Julian Watson